AN IN
AN

CW00566868

OTHER BOOKS OF INTEREST

AN INTRODUCTION TO
ANTENNA THEORY

by

H. C. WRIGHT

BERNARD BABANI (publishing) LTD
THE GRAMPIANS
SHEPHERDS BUSH ROAD
LONDON W6 7NF
ENGLAND

PLEASE NOTE

© 1987 BERNARD BABANI (publishing) LTD

First Published — August 1987

British Library Cataloguing in Publication Date
Wright, H. C.
   1. Antennas (Electronics)
   I. Title
   621.38'028'3   TK7871.6

ISBN 0 85934 173 9

Printed and Bound in Great Britain by Cox & Wyman Ltd, Reading

DEDICATION

This book is dedicated to Caroline and Alison

Preface

The known family of electromagnetic waves ranges from the very high-energy cosmic rays with wavelengths of 10^{-12} cms through X-radiation and visible light to the Extra Low Frequency (ELF) radio waves of 10^9 cms.

Mathematical analysis of the behaviour of the shorter wavelength radiations is often simplified and made more exact by the fact that the material objects with which they interact can be regarded as infinitely large compared with the wavelength. In the case of radio-waves the antenna and the wavelength are of comparable size and exact statements of behaviour cannot always be made. This absence of a body of precise lore governing the antenna makes the subject of particular interest to the amateur experimenter and innovator.

Any conducting body exposed to a radio-wave will have electric currents induced in it and, conversely, any conductor carrying varying currents will radiate. Thus an antenna can take any form from a bedstead to a tin-tack and, while these particular artefacts are seldom encountered in practice, the experimenter can test ideas and innovations with little more than bent copper wire, particularly with television and CB wavelengths.

This book attempts to deal with the basic concepts relevant to receiving and transmitting antennas in a manner which emphasises the mechanisms involved and minimises the mathematics used.

The bibliography provided offers the next stage of reading and understanding, while the outline set of original papers listed should allow a particular interest to be followed up in detail.

I would like to thank the staff of the Open University Library for the frequent help they gave me during the preparation of this book. Again I am deeply indebted to Mr B. C. Pope for scrupulous proof-reading.

H. C. Wright, Potterspury 1987

CONTENTS

1. Definition of the Antenna and Wave-Motion

The radio antenna may be defined as the interface between a circuit in which electrical power is constrained to follow conducting paths, and electromagnetic radiation travelling freely through space. The antenna may convert power in the circuit into radiated energy or vice versa, forming either a transmitting or receiving antenna respectively. Whereas the flow of electrical currents in a circuit is a comparatively familiar idea, the passage of electromagnetic energy through free space needs further thought, and, since it has the properties of a wave-motion, we shall first consider the basic behaviour of any wave pattern.

Consider a steady note being emitted by a loud-speaker. The air pressure will rise and fall regularly in the form of a sine-wave (Fig.1.1) and if we were to measure that pressure at some fixed distance from the speaker the variation would

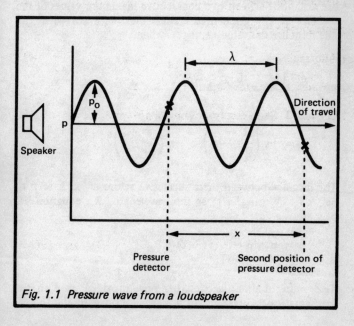

Fig. 1.1 Pressure wave from a loudspeaker

be observed. If p is the pressure at any time t then:

$$p = p_0 \sin 2\pi ft + P \tag{1.1}$$

for a note of frequency f Hertz, being sounded in an atmospheric pressure P. We note that p_0, the amplitude of the note, cannot exceed P or there would be periods of negative pressure which is not possible. If the point at which the pressure is measured is now moved a distance x away from the speaker then we measure a pressure that has travelled from the original point at the velocity of sound, say v. It is in fact the pressure that existed there a time x/v earlier. We can express this by changing the time t in equation 1.1 to $(t - x/v)$

At x
$$p = p_0 \sin 2\pi f \left(t - \frac{x}{v}\right) + P \tag{1.2}$$

Now we only need to find the wavelength of the note, that is the distance between two consecutive maximum values of the pressure at any given time. These maxima occur when the sine term has the value +1, that is when:

$$2\pi f \left(t - \frac{x}{v}\right) = \frac{\pi}{2}, \quad \frac{5\pi}{2}, \ldots$$

or when

$$x = -v\left(\frac{1}{4f} - t\right), \quad -v\left(\frac{5}{4f} - t\right) \ldots$$

The distance between these successive values of x is seen to be v/f. Writing v/f as the wavelength λ, equation 1.2 becomes

$$p = p_0 \sin \frac{2\pi}{\lambda} (vt - x) + P \tag{1.3}$$

This rather tedious section has now provided us with the mathematical expression for a wave-motion with the follow-

2

ing properties:

> velocity of propagation v
> wavelength λ
> frequency of variation $f = v/\lambda$

As we shall in future be dealing with the variation in electric and magnetic fields, which can assume negative values, rather than air pressure, the atmospheric term P may be dropped and the general wave equation written as:

$$p = p_0 \sin \frac{2\pi}{\lambda} (vt - x) \qquad (1.4)$$

2. Electromagnetic Waves

If the air pressure p is replaced by an electric field E we have the beginnings of an electromagnetic wave. In fact this will be only half the system since any changing electric field must have a magnetic field associated with it. This magnetic field is at right angles to the electric field but has its maximum and minimum values at the same time and in the same place as the electric field, see Figure 2.1. The relative amplitudes E_0 of the electric field and B_0 of the magnetic flux density are linked by the relationship:

$$\frac{\text{Electric Field}}{\text{Magnetic Flux}} = \text{Speed of wave propagation} .$$

The speed of this wave in free space is 3×10^8 metres/sec, the same as that of light, and so:

$$E_0/B_0 = 3 \times 10^8 \text{ metres/sec} .$$

As an example of the magnitudes involved, if E_0 were 10^{-6}

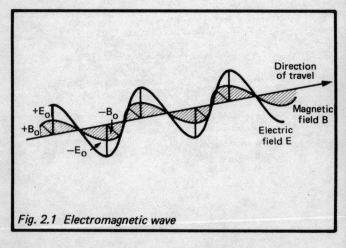

Fig. 2.1 Electromagnetic wave

volts/metre then B_0 would be:

$$10^{-6}/3 \times 10^8 = 3.3 \cdot 10^{-15} \text{ Tesla} .$$

This twin magnetic and electric wave, with each component behaving like the pressure wave shown in Figure 2.1, constitutes the energy flow which is either produced by the transmitting antenna or collected by the receiving antenna.

3. An Elementary Transmitting Antenna

Consider the two electrodes A and B shown in Figure 3.1a and let an alternating voltage be applied to them. Close to A and B an electric field would be observed to rise to a maximum in one direction, collapse to zero and then increase to a maximum in the·opposite direction. As the field collapses its electric energy returns to the circuit (barring some small losses due to the inefficiency in any real circuit) and is then used to .build up the field in the opposite direction, the process being repeated through each cycle of the alternating voltage.

At some point remote from A and B however (Figure 3.1b), when the applied voltage starts to decrease the energy in the field cannot return to the electrodes before their potential difference has fallen to zero. As there are now no charges on the electrodes for lines of electric force to start or end on, the existing line is forced to form a closed loop. As the new, opposite, field starts to build up between the electrodes it repels the closed loop away into space. The process is constantly repeated with the alternating voltage to give a train of loops which yield the electric wave form shown in Figure 2.1. Because this is a varying electric field it creates a magnetic field at right angles to itself and so completes the travelling electromagnetic energy, or radio wave, shown.

We have so far spoken vaguely of spaces close to, and remote from the electrodes. To be more exact, let L be the maximum distance from which electric energy can return to the circuit as the electrode voltage falls. Then, to find L , observe that the time to travel a distance L is

$$L/c$$

and also that if the voltage alternates with a frequency f then the time taken for a field reversal is

$$\tfrac{1}{2}(1/f) .$$

It is necessary for the travel time to be less than, or equal to,

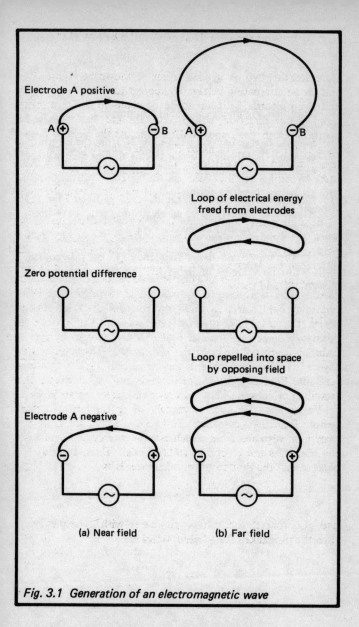

Electrode A positive

A ⊕ ⊖ B A ⊕ ⊖ B

Loop of electrical energy
freed from electrodes

Zero potential difference

Loop repelled into space
by opposing field

Electrode A negative

⊖ ⊕ ⊖ ⊕

(a) Near field   (b) Far field

Fig. 3.1 Generation of an electromagnetic wave

the field reversal time for the energy to return to the circuit and so:

$$L \leqslant c/2f .$$

This, simplified, argument can then be summed:

(i)   Electric energy beyond a radius $c/2f$ from the electrode assembly is returned to the circuit during each voltage cycle and so is of no value for transmission.

(ii) Electric energy beyond a radius $c/2f$ is freed from the circuit and travels out as an electromagnetic wave-train, to give the transmitted signal.

Knowing the wave-train has a frequency f and, of course, travels with the velocity of light c , then the wavelength is equal to c/f and so

$$L = \lambda/2 .$$

4. Introducing the Half-Wave Dipole

From the previous section it is clear that an important concern for the antenna designer must be to ensure that only a small fraction of the total field energy lies in the, ineffective, near field zone. This may be achieved by ensuring that:

(i) the geometry of the antenna is aimed at the creation of a widely dispersed field;

(ii) the near field zone is made small.

The geometry of the elementary antenna just considered was poor, with the field concentrated in a small space immediately between the two "point" electrodes. A much better design, which is frequently used in practice, consists simply of two rods or wires set in line as shown in Figure 4.1. The field lines spread from all points of each rod or wire into the surrounding space and the longer the rods the greater the

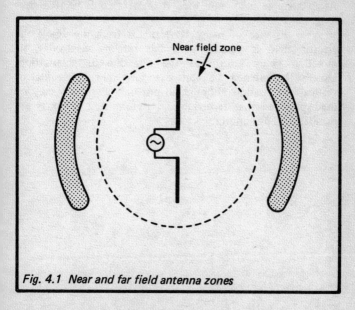

Fig. 4.1 Near and far field antenna zones

energy spread and the better the antenna. There is however a limit to the useful length of each rod since, for lengths greater than $\lambda/4$, the electrons cannot follow the changes of potential from the alternating voltage source. In other words, the more slowly the potential reverses the farther the electron charge can travel and the greater the useful length of the antenna.

Turning to the size of the near field zone, the only factor affecting this is the frequency f which, for a minimum zone size, should be large. In practice the value of f chosen for operation may be decided by other considerations such as the efficiency of the circuit producing the alternating voltage, the efficiency with which radiation of that frequency is propagated through the space between transmitter and receiver and also, of course, man-made laws governing the frequency which any particular operator may use.

Having decided on, or been forced to accept, some particular frequency, a two-rod antenna with an overall length of $\lambda/2$ will give the conventional and efficient radiating or receiving device generally referred to as a half-wave dipole. As an example an antenna used at 15 MHz would be 10 metres long.

At a distance of many wavelengths from the dipole the electric field is parallel with the antenna electrodes, its direction being known as the direction of polarisation. Usually the antenna is mounted to give either horizontal or vertical polarisation although in principle any angle may be used provided that receiving and transmitting antennas are parallel with one another.

5. Antenna Efficiency

If a transmitting antenna is connected to an AC generating circuit and both the voltage across the antenna terminals and the current flowing into them are measured then the apparent resistance of the antenna may be determined as the ratio of voltage to current amplitude in the usual way. Measuring the total radiated power (a difficult but not impossible experiment) will usually reveal a discrepancy in as much as it will be less than the product of the current and voltage. This discrepancy is caused by the power loss which occurs in the structure of most real antennas as a consequence of the heating effect of the current.

It is convenient to represent the antenna by an equivalent circuit consisting of an apparent resisistance R_R, associated with the radiated power, in series with a real resistance R_L which gives rise to the power loss, see Figure 5.1.

We shall later show that the "lossy" resistance can be reduced to zero in principle and it will be convenient for the moment to forget it and concentrate on R_R. This is a unique "resistance" in as much as when a current is fed into it, instead of heating taking place, the power appears as radiated electromagnetic energy. It is in fact only an algebraic concept, being the magnitude of the real resistance

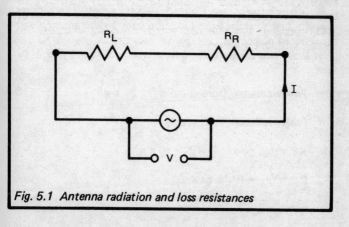

Fig. 5.1 *Antenna radiation and loss resistances*

which would affect the AC generating circuit in the same way as the antenna does if it were to replace the antenna.

This is why it was earlier referred to as an "apparent" resistance but it is nevertheless very important.

The efficiency of the antenna η is defined by

$$\text{Efficiency} = \frac{\text{Radiated Power}}{\text{Total Power Supplied by Circuit}}$$

$$\eta = \frac{(\text{Circuit current})^2 \times R_R}{(\text{Circuit current})^2 \times (R_R + R_L)}$$

$$\eta = \frac{R_R}{R_R + R_L}.$$

Accurate measurement of the efficiency of a transmitting antenna is a difficult experimental task since it requires precise knowledge of the power accepted by the antenna from its transmitting circuit and of the total power then radiated from it.

The Wheeler technique for efficiency measurement is a useful method for short wavelength antennas. Basically the power being fed into the test antenna is measured while it is radiating freely, see Figure 5.2. Next a metallic enclosure is positioned to reflect the radiation back to the antenna and the reduced power then accepted is measured.

If these two measured powers are respectively P_1 and P_2 then:

Power radiated from antenna $= P_1 \times \eta$

Power reflected back is also $= P_1 \times \eta$

Reflected power $= (P_1 \times \eta) \times \eta$

$\therefore \quad P_2 = P_1 - (P_1 \times \eta) \times \eta$

or $\quad \eta = \sqrt{I - P_2/P_1}$.

12

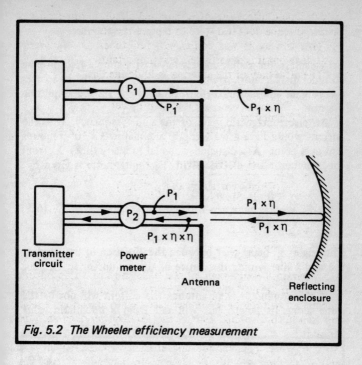

Fig. 5.2 The Wheeler efficiency measurement

This method is used mainly for short wavelength work because the reflecting enclosure must be at a distance of several wavelengths from the antenna or it will absorb some of the near-field energy discussed in Section 3, and give a false measurement.

Apparatus separation distances are important in all efficiency measurements since two antennas placed within a wavelength or so of one another will affect each other in the same way that primary and secondary windings in a transformer do, without any radiative connection at all. It is thought that this effect may have been what was actually observed in early reports of long wave radio communication.

6. Radiation Resistance

To calculate the radiation resistance of a simple rod antenna consider first a short straight conductor, of length L metres carrying an alternating current frequency f Hz and amplitude I amps.

An electromagnetic wave of the same frequency f as the current would have a wavelength λ equal to $3 \times 10^8/f$ metres and at a point A a distance r, equal to many times λ, from the conductor the electric field E_θ volts/metre is given by:

$$E_\theta = \frac{60\pi \, IL \, \text{Sin} \, \theta}{r\lambda} \quad \text{volt/metre} \qquad (6.1)$$

The angle θ being that between the direction of the conductor and a line joining the centre of the conductor to A, see Figure 6.1.

If the conductor is an antenna the current will not be the same along its length but will fall from a maximum value

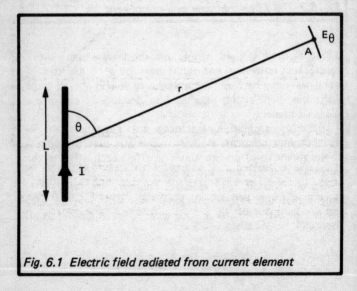

Fig. 6.1 Electric field radiated from current element

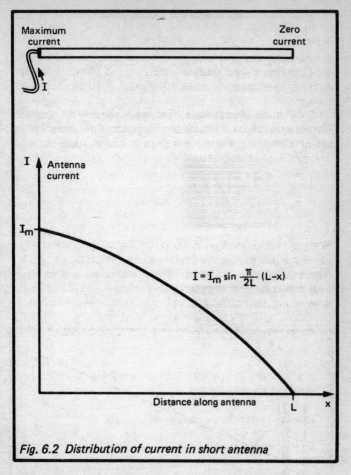

Fig. 6.2 Distribution of current in short antenna

I_m, where it is fed in at one end down to zero at the far end, since there it has nowhere to flow. Allowing the current to follow a simple sine law, as shown in Figure 6.2, will give it an average value of $I_m \times 2/\pi$. Using this value equation 6.1 becomes, for an antenna element,

$$E_\theta = \frac{60\pi \, I \times 2/\pi \, L \, \text{Sin} \, \theta}{r\lambda} \quad \text{volt/metre} \qquad (6.2)$$

15

F , the electromagnetic power density flowing out at A , is then given by:

$$F = \frac{(E_\theta)^2}{Z_S} \quad \text{watt/metre}^2 \tag{6.3}$$

where Z_S is the impedance of free space equal to 377 ohms.

Because of the variation in θ this power flux varies from zero for directions where $\theta = 0$ or π , to a maximum of

$$\left(\frac{60\pi \, I \times 2/\pi \, L}{r\lambda} \right)^2 \Big/ Z_S$$

when $\theta = \dfrac{\pi}{2}$.

The average value is again $2/\pi \times$ maximum and so the average power flow $\overline{F}$ is given by:

$$\overline{F} = \frac{2}{\pi} \times \left(\frac{60\pi \, I \times 2/\pi \, L}{r\lambda} \right)^2 \Big/ 377 \quad \text{watt/metre}^2 .$$

The total power P passing through a sphere of radius r centred on the antenna is

Average power flux × surface area of sphere

$$= \overline{F} \times 4\pi r^2$$

$$= 300 \left(I \, \frac{L}{\lambda} \right)^2 \quad \text{watts} .$$

If the radiation resistance is R_R then the power radiated must be $I^2 R_R$ therefore:

$$I^2 R_R = 300 \left(I \, \frac{L}{\lambda} \right)^2 \text{ watts}$$

and so

$$R_R = 300 \left(\frac{L}{\lambda} \right)^2 \text{ ohms} .$$

7. Complex Impedance of the Antenna

While the half-wave dipole discussed in a previous section behaves as a pure resistance, any antenna shorter than half a wavelength will have a capacitative element in its equivalent circuit while a longer antenna will show inductive behaviour, see Figure 7.1. The reason for the reactive behaviour of the antenna when it is not half a wavelength long can be seen if we consider the action of the electrons in a conducting rod when placed in a static electric field. A current will flow in the rod under the influence of the field until, after a time equal to:

(rod length, ℓ)/(velocity of light, c)

the electron charge will have reached a new equilibrium condition as illustrated by Figure 7.2.

If however the field direction is reversed before this equilibrium is reached, and continues to be regularly reversed, it will lead the current that flows in the rod in the manner characteristic of an inductive load. If the reversal time of the field is less than ℓ/c then the field will lag behind the current as in a capacitative load.

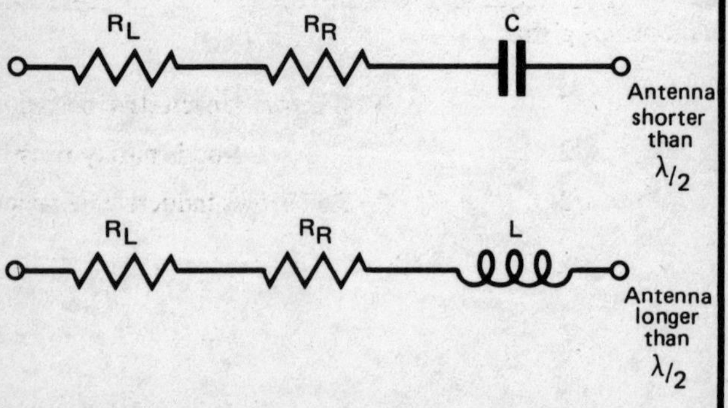

Fig. 7.1 Antenna equivalent circuits

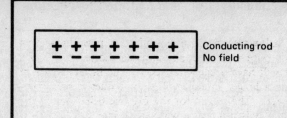

Conducting rod
No field

Field applied displacing
mobile electrons to new
equilibrium position

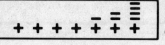

Fig. 7.2 Charge distribution in antenna

To express this formally let the frequency of field reversal be f, then:

If $1/2f < \ell/c$ field leads current. Rod inductive.

If $1/2f > \ell/c$ field lags behind current. Rod capacitative.

If $1/2f = \ell/c$ field and current in phase. Rod resistive.

The wavelength λ of e.m. radiation associated with a field reversal frequency f can replace c/f in these three relationships giving:

$\ell < \lambda/2$ Rod shows capacitative behaviour.

$\ell = \lambda/2$ Rod is purely resistive.

$\ell > \lambda/2$ Rod shows inductive behaviour.

8. Directionality, Gain and Capture Cross-Section

Although it is not possible either in principle or practice to make an antenna that radiates uniformly in all directions, the motion of such a device will be useful when considering the directional properties of real antennas. The polar diagram of an antenna shows what proportion of the total emitted power is sent in any particular direction. The diagram is

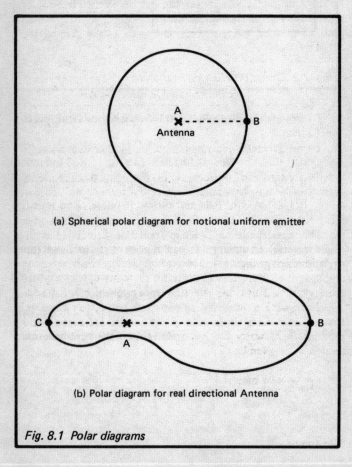

(a) Spherical polar diagram for notional uniform emitter

(b) Polar diagram for real directional Antenna

Fig. 8.1 Polar diagrams

formed by an imaginary surface surrounding the antenna such that the length of a line drawn between the antenna and a point on the surface is proportional to the power radiated in the direction of that line. The polar diagram of the notional uniform emitter shown in Figure 8.1a is a sphere with the antenna at the centre so that the distance from antenna to any point on the surface is the same. Figure 8.1b shows a more realistic polar diagram in which most of the radiation is directed along AB and very little in the reverse direction AC.

The ratio of the power from an antenna in the direction of maximum emission to that from a uniform emitter, when both have equal input powers, is known as the gain of the antenna.

For the antenna in Figure 8.1b the gain G is given by:*

$$G = \frac{\text{Power radiated in direction AB}}{\text{Power which would be radiated by uniform emitter}}$$

The gain is generally expressed in decibels rather than a simple ratio.

This concept is of obvious use in comparing the directional properties of any two antennas but the term "gain" is misleading since in most fields it implies an increase in power made by the device itself, clearly not possible with a passive piece of metal.

So far gain and directionality have been considered in terms of transmitting antennas. If we are dealing with receiving antennas it is more logical to think in terms of the capture cross section. This is the effective area from which e.m. power is collected by a receiving antenna. Suppose, for example, that an antenna is in a field of W watts per metre² and produces w watts at its terminals then the capture cross section A is given by:

$$A = w/W \text{ metre}^2$$

*See Appendix 1.

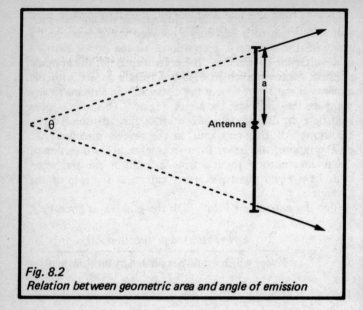

Fig. 8.2
Relation between geometric area and angle of emission

Now the gain G and the capture cross section A have a fixed relationship for any antenna:

$$A = G \frac{\lambda^2}{4\pi}.$$

The proof of this relationship is complex but it is in fact a particular case of a general concept in the collection and direction of e.m. radiation, extending even to the very short wavelengths of visible light.

If a source of e.m. radiation of wavelength λ is placed at the centre of a circular reflector of radius a as in Figure 8.2 then θ, the solid angle of radiation, is related to λ and a by:

$$\theta = \frac{\sqrt{\pi}\,\lambda}{a} \quad \text{radians}.$$

It is seen from this that the more directional the system is, i.e. the smaller θ, the larger πa^2, the capture cross section, must be.

By comparing the last two equations it is seen that the gain may be related to the solid angle of emission θ by:

$$G = [2\pi/\theta]^2 .$$

9. Matching

To obtain the maximum power from an electrical source it is necessary that the impedance of the load should match that of the source. The most simple situation to consider is one where both source and load are purely resistive as, for example, when a battery of V volts e.m.f. and R ohms internal resistance is connected to a load of R_L ohms as shown in Figure 9.1a.

I, the current in the circuit is given by

$$I = V/(R + R_L).$$

The power available in the load resistance is

$$I^2 R_L = V^2 R_L/(R + R_L)^2.$$

This power is a maximum* when $R_L = R$, that is when the source and load resistances are the same.

*This can be seen by differentiating the power with respect to R_L or, better by plotting out some numerical examples.

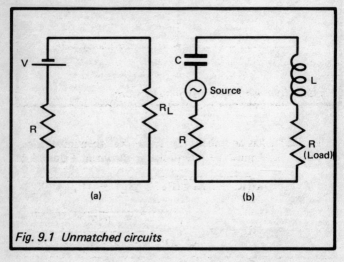

Fig. 9.1 *Unmatched circuits*

In AC circuits the source of electrical power may have a significant reactive component, as a non-resonant antenna would have, and then the matching requirement is that the reactive components of source and load should also be equal in magnitude but opposite in sign, that is, a capacitive element in the source is matched by an inductive element in the load, see Figure 9.1b, and vice versa.

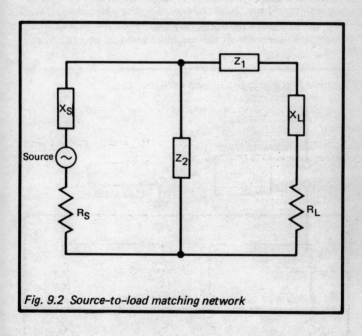

Fig. 9.2 Source-to-load matching network

If a source has an impedance $R_S + jX_S$ then impedances Z_1 and Z_2 must be interposed as shown in Figure 9.2.

$$Z_1 = \sqrt{(R_S + jX_S)([R_S + jX_S] - [R_L + jX_L])}$$

$$Z_2 = (R_L + jX_L)\sqrt{\frac{R_S + jX_S}{(R_L + jX_L) - (R_S + jX_S)}}$$

It should be noted that as the reactance of a circuit element varies with the frequency of the AC used, this network can only match perfectly at one frequency. Also, in practice, care must be taken that the loss in the interposed circuit does not outweigh the improvement in power transfer.

A further consideration arises if a coaxial cable is used to connect a symmetrical antenna, such as the dipole, directly to its transmitter or receiver, since then one arm of the dipole would have to be connected to the outer conductor of the cable which is usually earthed. Thus the dipole would become a monopole in the neighbourhood of an earthed rod.

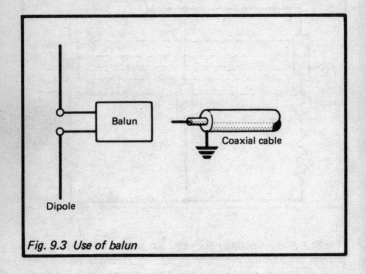

Fig. 9.3 Use of balun

To prevent this a balance-to-unbalance transformer, known for short as a "balun", is connected between cable and antenna, see Figure 9.3. The balun has a secondary benefit in preventing the radio frequency power in the cable leaking from the end of the cable and running back over its outer sheath as illustrated in Figure 9.4a.

The common sleeve balun consists of a metal sleeve one quarter of a wavelength long placed over the end of the cable as shown in Figure 9.4b.

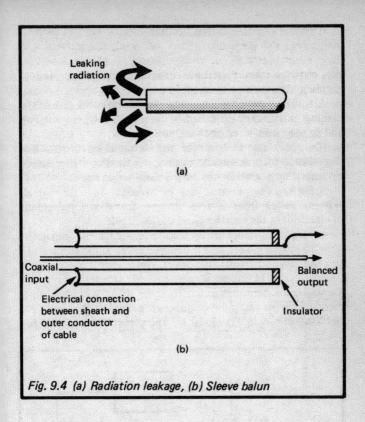

Fig. 9.4 (a) Radiation leakage, (b) Sleeve balun

The sleeve balun uses the fact that a quarter wavelength of coaxial cable, short-circuited at one end, reflects back all the radio-frequency power fed into it and so acts as an infinitely large impedance.

10. Noise

All electrical and electronic devices suffer from random currents which are unrelated to any desired signal in their circuit. These currents first became a problem because of the rushing sounds they produced in the reception of radio signals and so they were referred to as "noise".

Nowadays any interference with a signal by a signal-like disturbance such as sound in radio, needle-flicker in a meter, or "snow" in a television picture is classified as noise.

Some sources of noise can be avoided, but one that all systems suffer from is that due to the erratic movement of electrons in the resistive parts of the circuit.

A simple resistance behaves as if it were an AC generator with an output power which depends on both its temperature and the range of frequencies which the circuit it is connected to can accept. Consider a resistance R at a temperature of T degrees Kelvin connected to some load R_L through a filter which passes only frequencies between F_1 and F_2 Hertz as shown in Figure 10.1. The power W available for

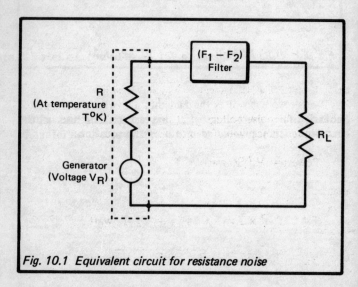

Fig. 10.1 Equivalent circuit for resistance noise

the load R_L is proportional to:

$$T \times (F_2 - F_1).$$

Putting in a constant of proportionality k makes this an equation:

$$W = k \times T \times (F_2 - F_1).$$

k is known as Boltzmann's constant and is equal to 1.4×10^{-23} watt sec/°K, making the complete equation:

$$\text{Noise Power} = 1.4 \times 10^{-23} \times T \times (F_2 - F_1) \text{ watt}.$$

So far R, the magnitude of the resistance, has not appeared in the analysis since the noise power depends only on the temperature. The individual noise current and noise voltage that give this power however, do contain R.

If the resistance were to be short-circuited the noise current I_n passing through it would need to satisfy the equation:

$$\text{Power} = I_n^2 \times R \text{ watt}$$

that is:

$$1.4 \times 10^{-23} \times T \times (F_2 - F_1) = I_n^2 \times R \text{ watt}$$

or $\quad I_n = 3.7 \times 10^{-12} \sqrt{(F_2 - F_1) \times T/R}$ amp.

Similarly the noise voltage V_n appearing across the open-circuited resistance would need to obey the equation:

$$\text{Power} = V_n^2/R \text{ watt}$$

that is:

$$1.4 \times 10^{-23} \times T \times (F_2 - F_1) = V_n^2/R \text{ watt}$$

or $\quad V_n = 3.7 \times 10^{-12} \sqrt{R \times T \times (F_2 - F_1)}$ volt.

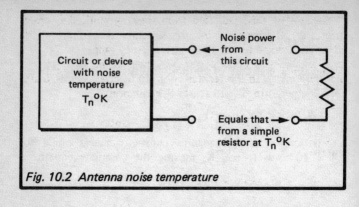

Fig. 10.2 Antenna noise temperature

It is usual to express the noise power generated by any circuit as though it were a simple resistor at some fictitious temperature T_n as illustrated by Figure 10.2. Suppose for example a circuit produces W_n watts of noise between frequencies F_2 and F_1. The temperature T_n of the imaginary noise-producing resistance that is equivalent to the circuit would be given by:

$$W_n = 1.4 \times 10^{-23} \times T_n \times (F_2 - F_1) \text{ watt}$$

$$T_n = 7 \times 10^{22} \times W_n/(F_2 - F_1) \,^\circ K \,.$$

The "circuit" we are most interested in is, of course, the antenna and the noise voltage it produces. It is not necessary to consider the current noise at this level since, in general, the antenna is not connected to a short-circuit but a high impedance circuit. Because of this, noise from the small ohmic resistance of the metal antenna structure can be ignored.

Apart from the noise voltages and currents in circuit components, any object at a finite temperature, that is above absolute zero, emits electromagnetic radiation. The wavelength of most of the emitted radiation is very short, indeed at room temperatures the bulk of it has a wavelength about one ten thousandth that of a TV signal, but there is always some radiation with the working wavelength or frequency of the antenna.

Because of this, radiation from trees, ground, sky, outer space, is all accepted by the antenna according to its directionality and its band-pass or frequency range.

If it collects a noise power W, then, in the same way as the noise power in the resistance, it can be given an imaginary noise temperature T_A to satisfy the equation:

$$W = 1.4 \times 10^{-23} (F_2 - F_1) \times T_A \text{ watt}$$

and so

$$T_A = 7 \times 10^{22} \times W/(F_2 - F_1) \text{ K}.$$

Antenna noise temperatures vary widely in practice, from tens to thousands of degrees Kelvin.

11. Quantitative Example of Local Communication

This section will deal with the powers, voltages and currents involved in a base transmitter broadcasting to a local receiver, such as a police or ambulance system.

Suppose a 100 MHz 50 watt transmitter is fed into a half-wave dipole broadcasting antenna, and the signal is received two miles away by a similar half-wave dipole, 200 feet above the level of the transmitter as illustrated in Figure 11.1. We will determine the voltage available at the terminals of the receiving antenna.

The length L of the antennas will be half the signal wavelength λ :

$$L = \lambda/2 = 1.50 \text{ metres} \qquad \text{(Sections 1, 3)}$$

The current I in the antenna must satisfy:

$$\text{Power} = \text{Radiation Resistance} \times \text{Current}^2$$

$$50 \text{ watts} = 75 \times I^2 \qquad \text{(Section 6)}$$

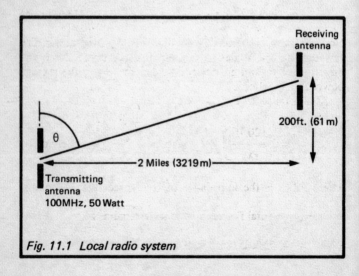

Fig. 11.1 Local radio system

$$I = 0.82 \text{ amp}.$$

The angle θ between the two antennas is given by:

$$\tan \theta = 10560/200$$

$$\sin \theta \simeq 1$$

r, the 2 mile distance between the antennas, must be taken as 3219 metres.

The power flux F at the receiving antenna can now be calculated:

$$F = 94 (IL \sin \theta / \lambda r)^2 \qquad \text{(Section 6)}$$

$$= 1.5 \text{ micro watts/metre}^2 .$$

Note that this signal is much greater than the noise power densities considered in Section 10 for any reasonable value of the band-pass $(F_1 - F_2)$.

The capture cross section A of the receiving antenna is given by:

$$A = \text{Gain} \times \lambda^2 / 4\pi \qquad \text{(Section 8)}$$

Now the gain G of a half-wave dipole is F_M, the power flux radiated at right angles to the antenna axis (since this is the direction of maximum power) divided by F_A, the average power flux (Section 8).

At a distance r :

$$F_M = \left(\frac{120 \, IL}{r\lambda}\right)^2 \bigg/ Z_S \text{ watt/m} \qquad \text{(Section 6)}$$

where Z_S is the impedance of free space $= 377$ ohms.

$$F_A = \text{Total Power/Area of sphere radius r}$$

$$= 75 \times I^2 / 4\pi r^2 \text{ watt/m}$$

$$G = F_M/F_A$$

$$= \left(\frac{120\,\text{IL}}{r\lambda}\right)^2 \Big/ Z_S \div \frac{75\,I^2}{4\pi r^2} = 1.6$$

$$A = G \times \lambda^2/4\pi = 1.15\ \text{m}^2 .$$

The power P collected at the receiving antenna is the product of this capture area A and the power flux F from the transmitting antenna.

$$P = F \times A = 1.7\ \text{microwatt} .$$

The voltage V at the terminals of the receiving antenna must then satisfy:

$$P = V^2/\text{Radiation Resistance}$$

and so:

$$V = \sqrt{1.7 \times 10^{-6} \times 75} = 11\ \text{millivolts} .$$

In this exercise the efficiency of each antenna has been taken as 100%, ignoring any lossy resistance in comparison with a 75-ohm radiation resistance. This is a reasonable approximation for a metal half-wave dipole operating at low power.

12. Reciprocity

It will have been noted that in dealing with radiation resistances and polar diagrams we have considered either transmitting or receiving antennas, according to which made the analysis the more simple. This convenient procedure may be justified by the Reciprocity Theorem. In essence this states that if a voltage V is applied between two points A_1 and A_2 in a passive circuit (that is one without a battery or power source) and the short circuit current I is measured between two other points B_1 and B_2 then, by applying V

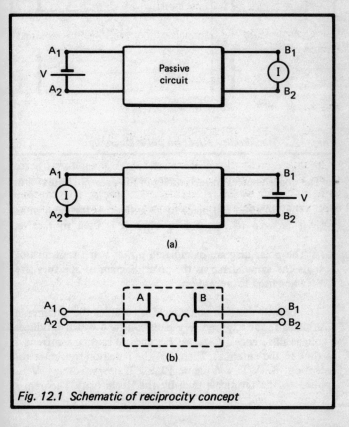

Fig. 12.1 Schematic of reciprocity concept

to B_1 and B_2, I will flow between A_1 and A_2, see Figure 12.1a.

The theorem is general and will hold if $A_1 A_2$ and $B_1 B_2$ are the terminals of two antennas A and B, linked by their radiative connection in place of a passive "black box" circuit, as illustrated in Figure 12.1b.

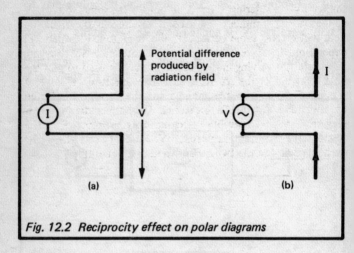

Fig. 12.2 Reciprocity effect on polar diagrams

The consequences of reciprocity in the present context are:

(i)   The radiation resistance of an antenna is the same when it is used to transmit as when it is used to receive.

(ii) The polar diagram of radiated power when transmitting is the same shape as the polar diagram of aperture size when used for reception.

To confirm the first consequence, consider the antenna in a receiving mode exposed to a radiation field which produces a voltage difference V across the ends so causing a current I to flow in the antenna. Then R_r, the radiation resistance for reception, is V/I, see Figure 12.2a. If now a voltage V is applied to the terminals then by the Reciprocity Theorem a current I will flow in the antenna giving a transmitting

36

radiation resistance R_t of V/I and so

$$R_r = R_t$$

as illustrated by Figure 12.2b.

The two polar diagrams of the antenna are shown to be similar by considering a fixed antenna with some voltage V applied to its terminals. A second antenna in the radiation field will receive some current I, the magnitude of which will depend on the angle between the two antennas. By changing this angle the varying magnitude of I may be used to plot the polar diagram of the receiving antenna's aperture. If now V is applied to the movable antenna and the current I received by the fixed antenna is measured, then the radiating polar diagram of the movable antenna can be plotted. The Reciprocity Theorem says that V and I can always be exchanged and so the two polar diagrams are identical.

13. Parasitic Elements

A rod approximately a half-wavelength long placed in the field of an electromagnetic wave will, as we have seen, absorb power from that field. If the rod is continuous with no connections to a circuit, it will re-emit some of the energy it absorbs, and this secondary emission may combine with the direct radio wave to increase the power collected by the antenna. In this way the effective cross-section of a receiving antenna may be increased and, by Section 8, an increase will be made in the directionality of a transmitting antenna.

These isolated rods are known as parasitic elements despite their beneficial effects.

If the parasitic element is resonant at a slightly lower frequency than that of the antenna, that is, it is a little longer than half a wavelength, it will act as a reflector of radiation and is placed behind the antenna in use. If the parasitic is shorter than half a wavelength, and so resonant at a higher frequency than that of the radiation in use, it will direct or concentrate the radiation. The use of both types of parasitic together will give a very directional or large aperture antenna. The arrangement may be compared with the use of a lens and reflector in an optical system, see Figure 13.1.

The general principle by which the parasitic element works may be understood by considering a transmitting antenna accompanied by just one parasitic element. The current flowing in the antenna depends on:

(i) The e.m.f. applied to the antenna terminals by the transmitter.

(ii) The current excited by the secondary emission reaching the antenna from the parasitic element.

In the parasitic element itself the current depends on that in the antenna.

This complex inter-relationship makes it difficult to determine mathematically the magnitude and phase of the current in the parasitic element for any given element length, and spacing between element and antenna. It is however,

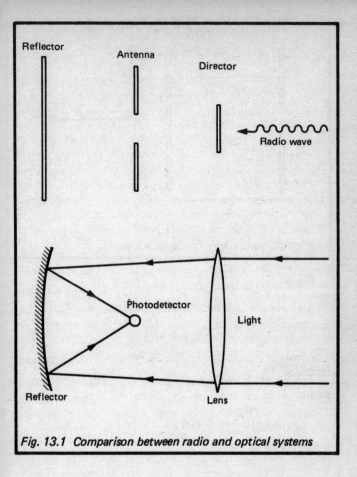

Reflector   Antenna   Director

Radio wave

Reflector   Photodetector   Light   Lens

Fig. 13.1 Comparison between radio and optical systems

relatively simple to calculate the phase difference that we would *like* to have between the currents in the antenna and the parasitic element, for either reflecting or directing properties.

Suppose, as shown in Figure 13.2, A is the antenna with a current of frequency f varying as:

$$\cos f.t$$

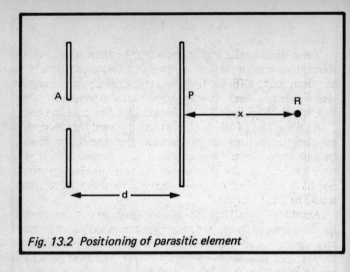

Fig. 13.2 Positioning of parasitic element

and P is a parasitic element at a distance d in which the induced current lags the antenna current by a time Δ :

$$\cos f(t - \Delta)$$

t being time.

At a point R the radiated power will be dependant on the sum:

$$\cos f(t - [d + x]/c) + \cos f(t - \Delta - x/c) .$$

Adding these two cosine functions gives a wave of amplitude

$$\cos f(\Delta - d/c) .$$

If we want the parasitic element to act as a director this amplitude must be as large as possible, that is equal to 1, a condition satisfied when

$$\Delta = d/c .$$

For action as a reflector the amplitude must be zero making

40

$$\Delta = d/c + 0.25/f .$$

These desired relationships between the phase lag Δ and the element separation d for director or reflector action are, as has been said, difficult to calculate, especially when several elements are in use. Generally, even after attempts to calculate, the final spacing and lengths are found by trial and error.

As the values of d used in practice are only fractions of a wavelength, the interaction between the elements is mainly by induction rather than radiation (see Section 3). If this were not so, then the presence of the parasitic element would not have any effect on the antenna current and calculations would be much simpler.

Anything that affects the antenna current must also change its radiation resistance and, again by the principle of reciprocity, its impedance for reception. The presence of a reflector element and several directors may reduce the values for a half-wave dipole from 75 to 20 or so ohms.

14. The Yagi-Uda Array

The actual power received from a radio signal is very small; for example a good television picture is obtained with a millivolt on an antenna connected to a set of 75 ohm impedance, giving a power of:

$$(10^{-3})^2/75 \sim 10^{-8} \text{ watt}$$

that is, about one hundredth of a microwatt.

In the early 1920's the Japanese professor Yagi and his student Uda devised a system for the radio transmission, not of information, but of substantial amounts of power. The technique used half-wave dipole transmitting and receiving antennas with, between them, a chain of parasitic-element directors each 0.45 of a wavelength long and spaced at 0.34 of a wavelength apart. Using this, Uda was able to charge a storage battery over a distance of some 40 feet, as illustrated by Figure 14.1. Although an interesting experiment, the

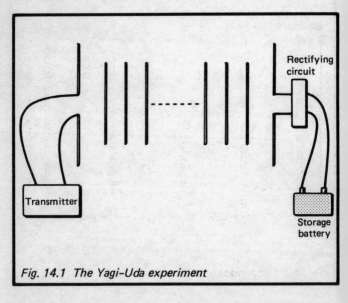

Fig. 14.1 The Yagi–Uda experiment

need for directors to be set up all the way between transmitter and receiver made it an impractical system. Despite the disadvantages for power transmission, Yagi and Uda carried on to develop their antenna system by adding a reflecting element behind the dipole and eventually producing the now famous Yagi-Uda array. Typical dimensions for such an array are shown in units of λ, the working wavelength, in Figure 14.2.

Directors may be added to an array to increase its gain, or aperture, with a limit imposed only by the space available, and the single rod reflector may be replaced by a sheet of metal or metal-mesh.

Since the radiation resistance of the antenna has been decreased to perhaps a quarter of its original 75 ohms by the presence of the parasitic elements it is desirable to modify the dipole to increase its resistance. This is usually done by connecting a second conductor across, and close to, the dipole as shown in Figure 14.3.

The whole is then known as a folded dipole and the inter-action of the radiating currents in the two arms reduces the

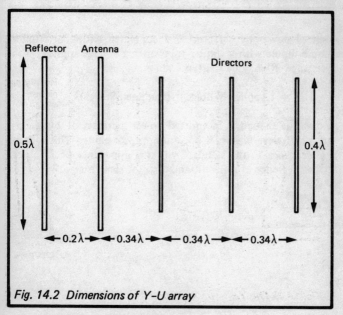

Fig. 14.2 Dimensions of Y–U array

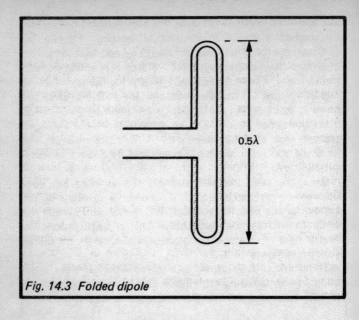

Fig. 14.3 Folded dipole

emitted power by a factor of 4 compared with that from a simple dipole with a similar transmitting voltage applied. The resistance R may be written:

$$R = (\text{Applied Voltage})^2 / (\text{Radiated Power})$$

and so the reduction in emitted power increases R by 4 and, for a half-wave dipole, it becomes ~ 300 ohms. This is then reduced back to the standard working impedance of 75 ohms by the presence of reflector and director elements.

15. The Ground Plane and the Earth as an Electrode

If an electric charge is brought close to a conducting metal plane it will induce charges of an opposite sign in the metal. These will be of a magnitude and position such that the electric field between charge and metal takes the symmetrical form that a single "mirror image" charge behind the metal plane would have caused. This is shown in Figure 15.1.

If the electrical charge considered were that due to the current flowing in one element of a dipole antenna, then the metal sheet would produce an image of that element to form the electrical equivalent of a complete dipole, as shown by Figure 15.2. The metal sheet acts like a mirror as far as electromagnetic radiation is concerned.

This dipole equivalent, formed from a ¼ wavelength element and a conducting sheet, is known as a "Marconi" antenna and, as the metal sheet is often replaced by the ground or earth, that is referred to as the ground plane. This ground plane is usually circular and needs to have a diameter

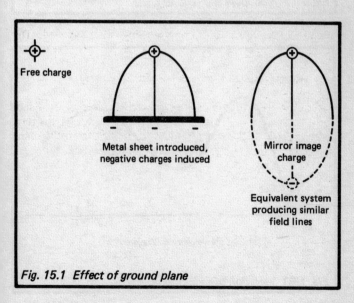

Free charge

Metal sheet introduced, negative charges induced

Mirror image charge

Equivalent system producing similar field lines

Fig. 15.1 Effect of ground plane

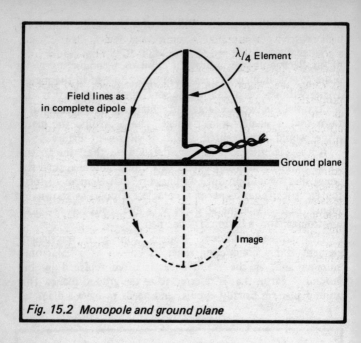

Fig. 15.2 Monopole and ground plane

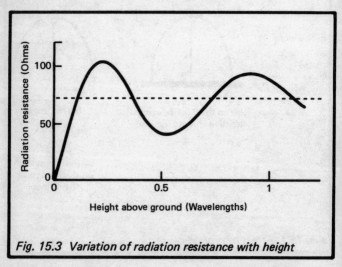

Fig. 15.3 Variation of radiation resistance with height

of a wavelength or more. This is why the earth, despite its high resistivity of around 10^5 ohm cm is used in place of, say, a copper sheet with a resistivity of only 10^{-6} ohm cm for low-frequency, long-wave antennas.

While the Marconi antenna actually needs the imaging properties of the earth in order to work properly, other antennas, when operated close to the ground, become less efficient because of the loss of power caused by the current-flow induced in the resistive earth.

One of the most significant effects of the presence of a conducting plane, like the earth, near an antenna system is the change made in the radiation resistance. The value of this resistance estimated in Section 6 ignored the ground effect, assuming that the antenna was being operated at such a height that there was no interaction. If however the antenna is only a wavelength or so high then the radiation resistance can vary widely as suggested in Figure 15.3.

16. Effect on Radiation Resistance of Current Distribution in Antenna

If the amplitude of the current flowing in a dipole antenna is measured along the length of the arms it is found to vary sinusoidally. Note that this is not a variation with time due to the frequency of the signal but a variation with position. The form of the current magnitude is shown in Figure 16.1 for antennas with lengths varying from $\lambda/2$ to 2λ. The formula relating the current magnitude I with d, the distance along the antenna, is:

$$I \propto \sin(\pi \times d/[\lambda/2]).$$

In each case the current flow at the end of the antenna is zero since there is nowhere for charge to flow into, or out from there. The magnitude of the current passes through half a sine-wave of variation for every $\lambda/2$ of antenna length and, for the 2λ antenna, the current at any instant is actually flowing in opposite directions in different parts of the antenna. The variation of current amplitude along the antenna makes the radiation resistance dependent on the point at which the antenna is broken in order to introduce the transmitting or receiving circuit.

The radiation resistance R_R of a $\lambda/2$ dipole was calculated in Section 6 to be about 75 ohms when the connection was made at the centre where the current flow is a maximum, say I_M. Suppose now that the connection is made a distance x from the end, see Figure 16.2, where the current would be:

$$I_M \times \sin(\pi \times x/[\lambda/2]).$$

Equating the radiated powers in the two cases gives:

$$I_M^2 \times 75 = I_M^2 \times \sin^2(\pi \times x/[\lambda/2]) R_x.$$

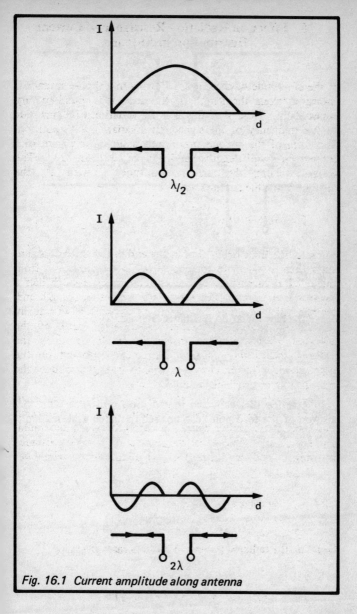

Fig. 16.1 *Current amplitude along antenna*

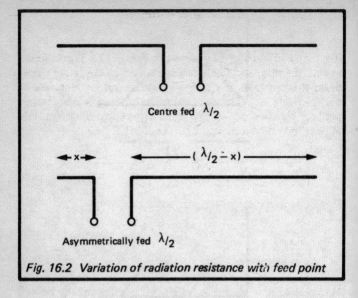

Fig. 16.2 Variation of radiation resistance with feed point

Hence the new radiation resistance R_x is:

$$\frac{75}{\sin^2(2\pi x/\lambda)} \text{ ohms .}$$

In practice this variation in radiation resistance with the position of the feed point can be used to match a given circuit to its antenna.

17. Frame Antennas

If a wire coil, such as that shown in Figure 17.1 is positioned so that the magnetic field associated with an e.m. wave passes through it, then an alternating potential will be produced at the terminals T. The mechanism is the same as that used to produce electrical power in a dynamo and ϵ, the magnitude of the e.m.f. produced, is proportional to:

    The strength of the magnetic flux B

    The area of the loop $\mathcal{A}$

    The frequency of the e.m. wave f and

    The number of turns in the coil N :

$$\epsilon = 2\pi B \mathcal{A} f N . \tag{17.1}$$

Now a straight wire antenna of length L in an electric field E would give an e.m.f. on $L \times E$. Thus a frame antenna of area A and number of turns N is equivalent to a straight wire antenna of length L if:

$$L \times E = 2\pi B \mathcal{A} f N . \tag{17.2}$$

We have seen in Section 2 that $E/B = c$ the velocity of light (and radio waves) and so :

$$L = 2\pi \mathcal{A} Nf/c = 2\pi \mathcal{A} N/\lambda . \tag{17.3}$$

The radiation resistance R_R (Section 6) is then:

$$300 \times (L/\lambda)^2 \simeq 300 \times (2\pi \mathcal{A} N/\lambda^2)^2 . \tag{17.4}$$

The capture cross-section of the frame is (Section 8) given by :

$$A = \text{Gain} \times \lambda^2/4\pi .$$

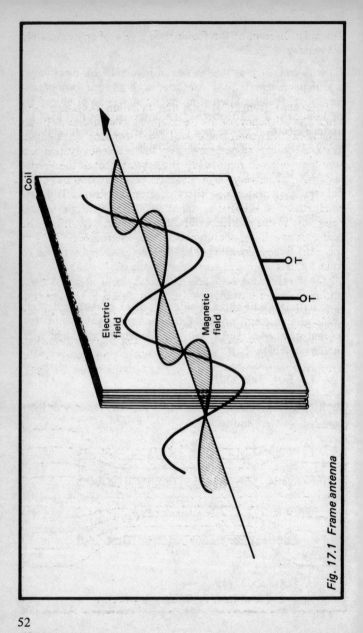

Fig. 17.1 Frame antenna

The polar diagram of the frame gives a gain of approximately 4/3 making:

$$A \simeq \lambda^2/3\pi.$$

It is seen from 17.4 that the radiation resistance, and hence the efficiency, of the frame is very small unless its linear dimensions are comparable with the operating wavelength. The need to choose between a very low efficiency system or a very large one was removed by the development of the Ferrite materials having very large magnetic permeabilities but without the electrical conductivity of iron or steel. This low conductivity is essential to avoid all, or most, of the power being lost in the induction of eddy currents. By filling the centre of the frame with a ferrite core the magnetic field of the e.m. wave is concentrated and increased by a factor of some 50 times, this is illustrated in Figure 17.2.

The ferrite core normally takes the form of a rod built into the receiver nowadays. It is seldom used in transmission since the characteristics of the material can change in the presence of large alternating fields.

It is seen from Figure 17.1 that if the frame is turned so that it is at right angles to the direction of propagation of the e.m. wave no magnetic flux will pass through it and the signal

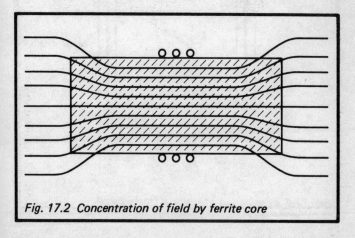

Fig. 17.2 Concentration of field by ferrite core

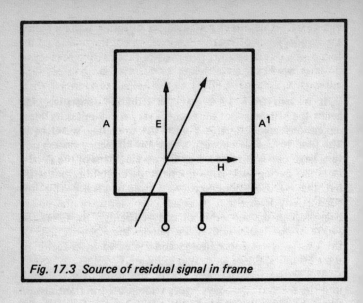

Fig. 17.3 Source of residual signal in frame

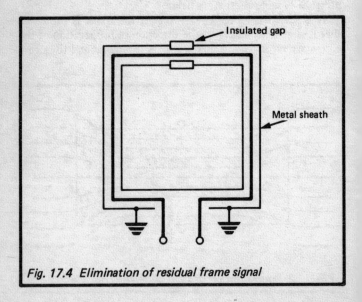

Fig. 17.4 Elimination of residual frame signal

will cease. This effect was used for direction finding before the development of radar. However, one of the failings of the frame when used for this purpose was that its minimum-signal position was not an absolute zero since, at that position, although the magnetic effect on the frame had vanished, there was a signal from the electric field in the vertical parts of the frame.

Figure 17.3 shows how the electric field E induces equal and opposite e.m.f.'s in the vertical members A and A' of the frame but, because the impedance to earth through the receiver circuit will not necessarily be the same for each side, the opposing currents may not be equal and a small residual signal will be present.

This effect was overcome by placing earthed conductors in the neighbourhood of the vertical parts of the frame so that each had a similar low impedance to earth. This may be regarded as putting a short-circuit open only to radio-frequencies across the circuit impedances in the receiver.

In practice these conductors often took the form of an earthed metal tube enclosing the frame with an insulated gap at the centre, see Figure 17.4. If the central gap is not present, circulating eddy currents can exist and mask the effects of the magnetic flux when the antenna is in a receiving position.

18. Superconducting and Active Antennas

It is clear from Section 5 that if the ohmic or "lossy" resistance of an antenna could be reduced to a negligible value then, even with a very low radiation resistance, an efficient antenna could be made. By using a superconducting material for the antenna this reduction in lossy resistance has been made experimentally. In detail, a small lead-plated frame antenna was cooled to $4.2°K$ when it became superconducting and showed near 100% efficiency, compared with the 1% of a copper antenna of similar size used at the same 400 Hz frequency.

This technique is not of great practical use at present because of the complex refrigeration required to cool the antenna down to the very low temperatures needed to induce superconductivity. However, materials having higher and higher superconducting transition temperatures are regularly reported and eventually the superconducting antenna will be a practical, as well as a laboratory, proposition.

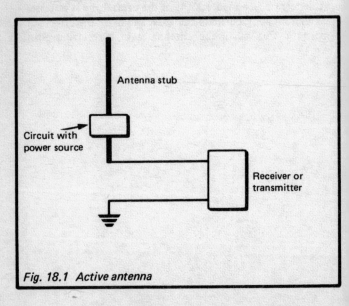

Fig. 18.1 Active antenna

An alternative technique for reducing the effective "lossy" resistance is to build-in electronic circuitry to form an active antenna, that is one containing a source of power as well as the passive metal and dielectric parts, see Figure 18.1. On first consideration it is difficult to see how an active antenna differs from a normal passive antenna connected to an amplifier. The basic difference lies in the fact that the current distribution (Section 16) in the antenna is changed by inserting an active circuit into its structure. This change can make the resonant frequency of the antenna much lower, allowing a reduction to quarter or less of the length over a broad range of frequencies.

With a passive antenna plus an amplifier the current distribution, and hence the antenna characteristics themselves, are unchanged both for transmission and reception.

The active antenna is most frequently used in vehicle radio where a full half-wave dipole would be unwieldy. It does not obey the reciprocity laws discussed in Section 12.

19. Dielectric Clad Antennas

Section 1 showed that the wavelength of a given frequency radiation depended inversely on the speed of propagation of the wave-motion. Because of this, a radio-wave passing through a material in which it travels more slowly than in free space, will have a shorter wave length and so, for use at any given frequency, an antenna surrounded by this material would also be smaller.

It is possible to imagine an experiment in which a transmitting and a receiving antenna were immersed in a great lake of pure water. The speed of radio-waves in a large volume of water is about 1/10th that in free space and so in this imaginary experiment both the transmitting and receiving antennas would be 1/10th of their "free-space" size, as illustrated by Figure 19.1.

It is difficult to keep large volumes of water pure, and any contamination would make them electrically conducting which would effectively stop the experiment. However, small sealed glass containers of water have been used to surround antenna elements and reduce the speed of radio-waves near them, so allowing the antenna to be made smaller.

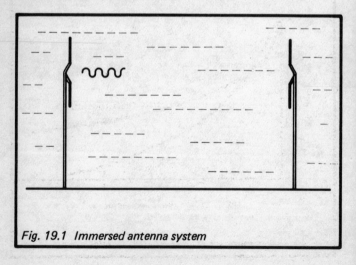

Fig. 19.1 Immersed antenna system

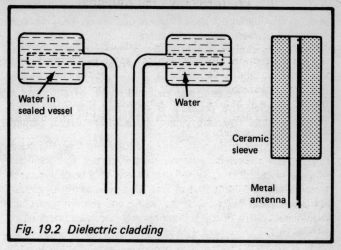

Fig. 19.2 Dielectric cladding

In some cases antenna elements have been sealed into ceramic sleeves which have the same effect as the water jackets in producing a reduction in radio-wave speed, see Figure 19.2.

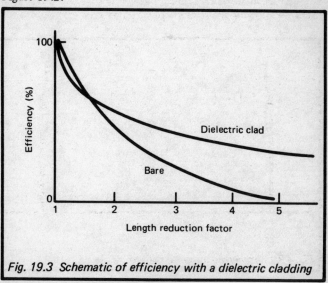

Fig. 19.3 Schematic of efficiency with a dielectric cladding

In practice antenna sizes have been reduced to 2/3rds or less by coating with a dielectric such as water, TiO_2 or some more sophisticated commercial ceramic.

The reduction in antenna size is, unfortunately, accompanied by a loss in efficiency, as shown in Figure 19.3. This is because some of the antenna power is wasted in heating the dielectric cladding material. Because of this loss in efficiency dielectric cladding is only desirable when a full size bare-metal structure cannot be accommodated, perhaps on an aircraft or other vehicle.

20. Effect of the Human Body on Personal Radio Antennas

The nearby presence of a human body, which may be thought of as a crude, poorly-conducting 2 metre monopole, has, understandably, a considerable influence on the characteristics of an antenna, with the impedance, the efficiency and the polar-diagram all being affected.

If the antenna-to-body distance is greater than about 5 cms the impedance of the antenna is not greatly affected although the total radiated power may be as much as halved. If the antenna is brought closer, and even into contact with the body the impedance changes greatly and the radiated power can fall to 10%.

At high frequencies, around 900 MHz or more, the body produces a comparatively straight-forward shadow effect on the polar-diagram as shown in Figure 20.1, while below 500 MHz its presence has less effect on the directionality.

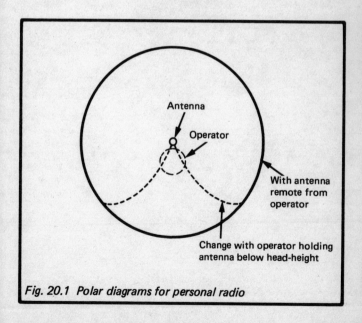

Fig. 20.1 Polar diagrams for personal radio

Measurements show that the clothing worn, the hand used to hold the apparatus and the posture of the operator using a personal radio all effect the behaviour of the antenna to some degree and there must be considerable room for more experimental work in this field.

21. The Slot Antenna

Instead of a conductor surrounded by free space, the slot antenna uses free space surrounded by a conductor. The free space member consists of a slot cut in a metal sheet, as illustrated in Figure 21.1a and, with the magnetic field of an e.m. wave parallel to this slot, currents induced in the surrounding metal can be led off by wires attached to each side. The diagram shows the leads at the centre of the slot but they may be placed at any point along its length. As the effective impedance varies with the lead position, as shown in Figure 21.1b, this gives a simple way of matching the antenna to its circuitry.

This design is particularly useful for vehicles where an awkwardly protruding rod antenna can be replaced by a slot cut in the bodywork.

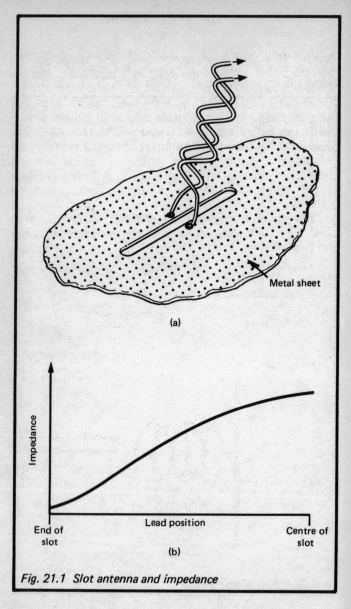

(a)

Metal sheet

(b)

Impedance

End of slot

Lead position

Centre of slot

Fig. 21.1 Slot antenna and impedance

22. The Helical Antenna

A shortened version of a quarter wavelength monopole antenna may be formed by winding the conductor into a helix. If the overall length of the helix is h, then the

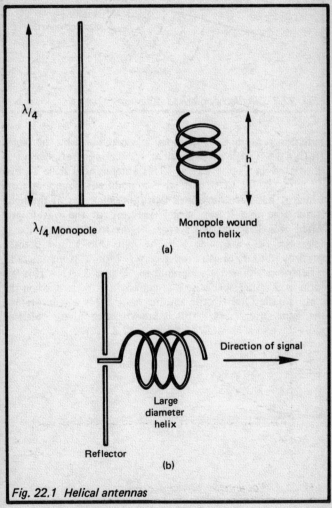

λ/4 Monopole

Monopole wound into helix

(a)

Direction of signal

Large diameter helix

Reflector

(b)

Fig. 22.1 Helical antennas

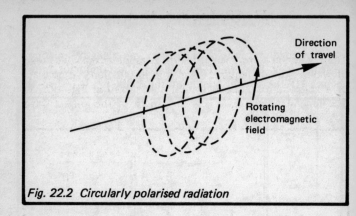

Fig. 22.2 Circularly polarised radiation

radiation resistance of the monopole is reduced by the factor $[h/(\lambda/4)]^2$ with an equivalent reduction in efficiency, as illustrated in Figure 22.1a. This antenna will have a polar diagram similar to that of the unmodified monopole from which it has been developed unless the diameter of the helix is so large that it approaches one-third of the wavelength. When this happens the system begins to act rather like a telescope or wave-guide and the helix has to be pointed towards the transmitter or receiver with a plane metallic reflector positioned at one end, see Figure 22.1b. This last form is a rather specialised antenna which is used when the e.m. radiation has electric and magnetic fields which rotate as the signal progresses. This is known as circularly polarised radiation and is illustrated by Figure 22.2.

23. The Log-Periodic Array

The log-periodic array is used when a response to a wide range of wavelengths is required from one installation. It consists of a collection of dipoles typically as shown in Figure 23.1. The longest dipole, a, is half the length of the longest wave

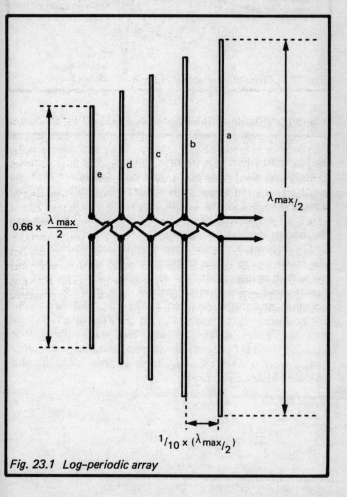

Fig. 23.1 Log–periodic array

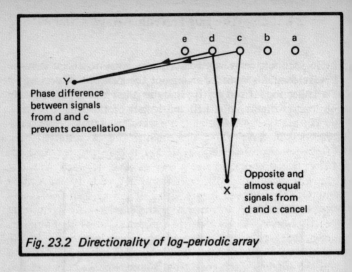

Fig. 23.2 Directionality of log-periodic array

λ_{max}, with which it is required to work. The next element, b, is 9/10th the length of a and at a distance 1/10th the length of a. In turn, c is 9/10ths the length of b and separated by a distance 1/10th the length of b . . . finally e is 9/10 x 9/10 x 9/10 x 9/10 x a = 0.66a, this being half the shortest working wavelength.

The elements are wired alternately in opposition as shown. The effect of this is best understood if the array is considered to be transmitting; adjacent elements will be sending out almost equal and opposite signals at right angles to the array axis thus minimising radiation to the side, such as at point X, as illustrated in Figure 23.2. In the axial direction, as at Y, the phase difference between signals coming from adjacent elements prevents them from cancelling each other. The array therefore radiates almost entirely along its axis, making it highly directional.

24. Long Wire and Travelling Wave Antennas

If a wire several wavelengths long is used as an antenna the polar diagram or directionality of the system will depend on whether the far end of the antenna is left free or is connected to earth through a matching impedance.

In the case of a free end, the wave generated by the transmitter will travel along the antenna and be reflected back from the open end since there is nowhere else for it to go. The two travelling waves, one moving forward and one moving back towards the transmitter, add up to form a stationary wave, see Figure 24.1. It can be seen that at any point such as A , to the side of the antenna, the signal from each positive peak is matched and cancelled by that from an adjacent negative peak and so no signal is radiated to the sides of the antenna. At points such as B , along the direction of the antenna, the signals from adjacent peaks have travelled distances differing by about half a wavelength and will thus be half a cycle out of phase and will add instead of cancelling and there will be radiation in both the forward and backward directions along the antenna.

When the antenna is connected to earth at the far end by a matching impedance the transmitted wave passes continuously along the wire and down to earth and so no reflected wave is set up and hence no stationary wave, as illustrated in Figure 24.2a.

Whereas in the free end case radiation took place in both directions along the length of the antenna, now, because the wave is moving, there is no radiation backwards, that is in the direction termination-to-transmitter. The reason for this can be seen by considering radiation from two points A and B which are separated by a quarter-wavelength, see Figure 24.2b. The radiation from A reaches a point C behind the antenna at the same time as radiation from B which had started a quarter of the period τ earlier. Because, in this time, the wave had moved a quarter of a wavelength forward the two radiations are of opposite polarity and cancel.

Since the long-wire travelling-wave antenna is the basis of several multi-element systems it warrants a more detailed

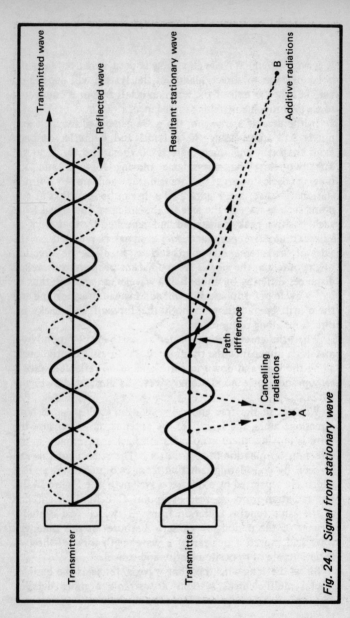

Fig. 24.1 Signal from stationary wave

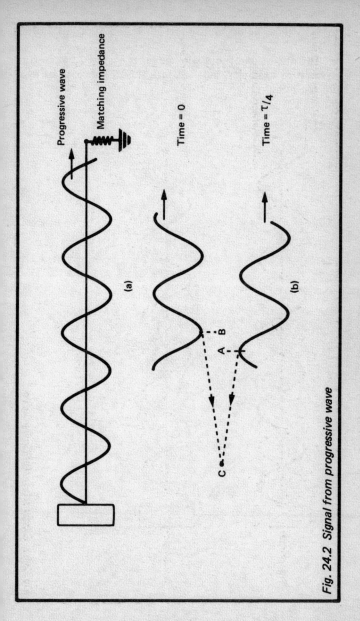

Fig. 24.2 Signal from progressive wave

analysis than the descriptive one above and Appendix 2 offers this.

The discussion of long-wire antennas has used transmitting systems as examples, but, as usual, similar concepts are valid for reception.

25. Microwave Antennas

When the frequency of the radiation in use reaches the order of 10^{10} Hertz the wavelength shrinks to only a few cms and the radiation can, to some extent, be treated as if it were a light beam. It can be passed along tubes (wave-guides), directed and collected with mirrors (microwave dishes) and used as a searchlight beam (radar scanning).

In addition to the use of a dish, or mirror, focussing of the microwave radiation may be carried out using a Fresnel lens exactly as in optical work. The Fresnel lens consists of a number of concentric opaque rings with transparent areas in between them. The size of these transparent rings or annuli is calculated so that radiation passing through interferes to produce a single bright spot or focus, see Figure 25.1.

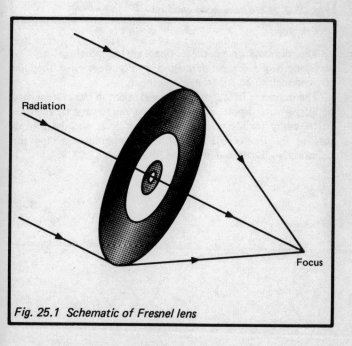

Fig. 25.1 Schematic of Fresnel lens

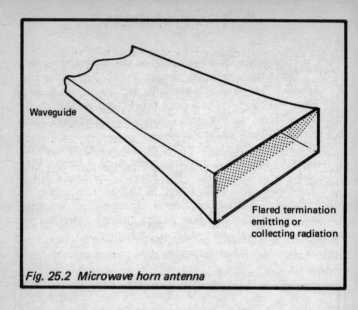

Waveguide

Flared termination emitting or collecting radiation

Fig. 25.2 Microwave horn antenna

The dimensions of these rings are proportional to the wavelength of radiation in use and in microwave work they are large enough to be cut from metal sheet.

The actual radiating or receiving element in the system may be a half-wave dipole, small enough at microwave frequencies to be easily made and accommodated, or it may be a horn formed by flaring the end of the wave-guide carrying the radiation, as illustrated in Figure 25.2.

26. Ten Micron Antennas

If the radiation frequency is increased even beyond the micro-wave region to 3×10^{13} Hertz the wavelength falls to 10^{-5} metres, or 10 microns, in the infrared region of the electro-magnetic spectrum. This form of energy is naturally emitted by any material when it is at a temperature of about 20°C but it cannot yet be produced by electronic techniques as can be microwaves. However, it can be detected by tiny dipole antennas, made using the miniature techniques of the semi-conductor industry. These dipoles take the form of a short metal whisker in contact with an oxidised metal surface forming an antenna with a rectifying diode attached, as illustrated by Figure 26.1.

Work in this area between the microwave and optical disciplines would seem to promise considerable interest for the future as miniaturisation skills become even more advanced.

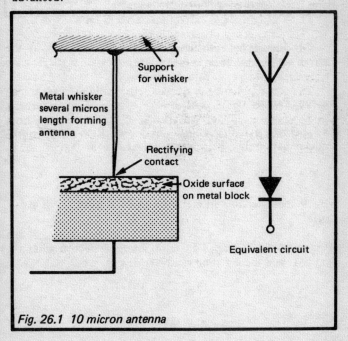

Fig. 26.1 10 micron antenna

Collected Formulae

Parameters of Electromagnetic Waves

Speed of propagation $= 3 \times 10^8$ metre sec^{-1}

Wavelength in free space for wave of frequency

f Hz $= 3 \times 10^8 / f$ metre

Ratio of electric field E *measured in volt metre^{-1} to the magnetic flux density* B, *measured in Tesla is given by:*

$E/B = 3 \times 10^8$ metre sec^{-1}

Power flux radiating from short AC bearing wire

$= 10^{-15} (IL \sin \theta f/r)^2$ watt metre^{-2}

Here L = length of wire measured in metre
I = amplitude of current measured in amps
f = frequency of current in Hz
θ = angle between current and flux directions
r = distance from wire in metres

Antenna Parameters

The aperture A is the ratio of the power P in the antenna to the radiation flux W incident on the antenna.

$A = P/W$,

with P measured in watt metre^{-2} and W in watts, A is in metre^2.

A can also be expressed in terms of the effective antenna length L and the radiation resistance R_R

$A = (L^2/R_R) \times 377$ metre^2

with L in metres and R_R in ohms.

For an antenna much shorter than half a wavelength:

$$A \rightarrow 0.12\lambda^2$$

For a half-wave dipole remote from the ground:

$$A \rightarrow 0.14\lambda^2$$

The Antenna gain G is related to the working wavelength λ and the aperture A by:

$$G = 12.6 \times A/\lambda^2$$

with A in metre^2 and λ in metre.

For a half-wave dipole:

$$G = 1.8$$

Antenna efficiency. For a transmitting antenna the efficiency is the ratio of the radiated power W_R to the total power W_T accepted by the antenna structure from the transmitting circuit.

$$\text{Efficiency } \eta = W_R/W_T .$$

For a receiving antenna it is the ratio of W_A, the power offered by the antenna to the receiving circuit, to W_T, the total power collected by the antenna.

$$\text{Efficiency } \eta = W_A/W_T .$$

Barring some exceptions discussed in the text, these two values of η are the same for a given antenna.

Radiation resistance R_R *of antenna*

For a half-wave dipole $R_R = 75$ ohms.

For a short dipole of effective length L metres operating at a wavelength λ metres R_R is $800(L/\lambda)^2$ ohms.

For an N turn frame antenna of geometric area $\mathscr{A}$ metre^2

$$R_R = 3.2 \times 10^4 \ (N\mathscr{A}/\lambda^2)^2 \text{ ohms.}$$

Experimental Papers

1. Efficiency Measurements (Section 5)

Two Methods for the Measurement of Antenna Efficiency.
E.H. Newman, P. Bohley & C.H. Walter.
I.E.E.E. Trans *AP 23* 457 1975.

An Analysis of the Wheeler Method for Measuring the Radiating Efficiency of Antennas.
G.S. Smith.
I.E.E.E. Trans *AP 25* 552 1977.

2. The Yagi-Uda Array (Section 14)

Beam Transmission of Ultra Short Waves.
H. Yagi.
Proc I.R.E. *16* 715 1928.

Design of Yagi Aerials.
R.M. Fishenden & E.R. Wiblin.
Proc. I.E.E. *96 pt III* 5 1949.

3. Ferrite Core & Loop Antennas (Section 17)

A Band II Ferrite Aerial Unit for Portable Receivers.
R.C.D. Thoday.
B.B.C. Report BBC RD 1977/II

Ferroxcube Aerial Rods.
H. van Suchtelen.
Electronic Application Bulletin *13* 88 1952.

Ferrite Rod Aerials.
H. Sutcliffe.
Int. J. Elect. Enging. Educ. *13* 35 1976.

Compact V.H.F. Aerial.
Electron, p13, November 10th 1977.

Design Values for Loop-Antenna Input Circuits.
J.E. Browder & V.J. Young.
Proc. I.R.E. Waves & Electrons Sect., p519, May 1947.

The Loop Aerial Revived.
R.E. Schemel.
Wireless World, p48, July 1979.

Loop Serial Reception.
G. Bramsley.
Wireless World, p469, November 1952.

4. Superconducting & Active Antennas (Section 18)
Superconducting Antennas.
G.B. Walker & C.R. Haden.
Journal of Applied Physics *40* 2035 1969.

Short Active Aerials for Transmission.
T.S.M. Maclean & P.A. Ramsdale.
Int. J. Electronics *36* 261 1974.

5. Dielectric Clad Antennas (Section 19)
Dielectric Clad Discone.
K.F. Woodman.
Electronics Letters. *13* 264 1977.

Dielectric Antennas.
Pennsylvania State University Report WFW 44. 1946.

6. Effect of the Human Body on Antennas (Section 20)
The Evaluation of Personal Aerials for the Police.
R.W. Smith.
Communications 74 Conference. Brighton. Paper 7.3.

Effects of a Human Body on a Dipole at 450 & 900 MHz.
H.E. King & J.L. Wong.
I.E.E.E. Trans *AP 25* 376 1977.

7. Helical Antennas (Section 22)

Characteristics of 1 to 8 Wavelength Uniform Helical Antennas.
H.E. King & J.L. Wong.
I.E.E.E. Trans *AP 28* 291 1980.

Small Helical Antennas.
T.S.M. Maclean & F. Rahman.
Int. J. Electronics *45* 381 1978.

8. Ten Micron Antennas (Section 26)

Properties of Infrared Cats-Whisker Antennas near 10.6μm.
B.L. Twu & S.E. Schwartz.
Appl. Phys. Letters. *26* 672 1975.

Bibliography

Antenna Theory, C.A. Balanis, Harper & Row, 1982.

Antennas, J.D. Krauss, McGraw Hill, 1950.

Antenna Engineering Handbook, H. Jasik (Ed.), McGraw Hill, 1961.

HF Antennas for All Occasions, L.A. Moxon, R.S.G.B., 1982.

25 Simple Amateur Band Aerials, E.M. Noll, Bernard Babani (publishing) Ltd, (BP125), 1983.

25 Simple Shortwave Broadcast Band Aerials, E.M. Noll, Bernard Babani (publishing) Ltd, (BP132), 1984.

25 Simple Indoor and Window Aerials, E.M. Noll, Bernard Babani (publishing) Ltd, (BP136), 1984.

25 Simple Tropical and M.W. Band Aerials, E.M. Noll, Bernard Babani (publishing) Ltd, (BP145), 1984.

Aerial Projects, R.A. Penfold, Bernard Babani (publishing) Ltd, 1982.

Fundamentals of Electric Waves, H.H. Skilling, John Wiley, 1948.

The Antenna, L. Thourel, Chapman & Hall, 1960.

Appendix 1. Antenna Gain

Let the power radiated from the antenna A shown in Figure A.1 in the direction ϕ, θ be:

$f(\phi, \theta)$ watt/unit solid angle

where θ is the angle with the horizontal and ϕ is the angle with a line drawn at right angles to the axis of the antenna.

The power passing through an elementary area $\cos \theta \, d\theta \, d\phi$ of a unit radius sphere in the direction ϕ, θ will be:

$f(\phi, \theta) \times \cos \theta \, d\theta \, d\phi$ watt

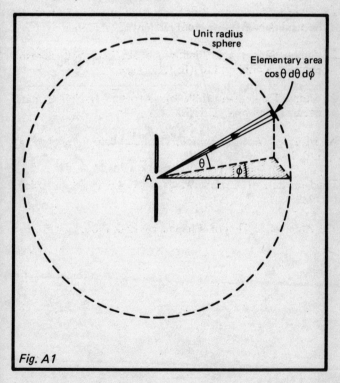

Fig. A1

Total power passing through the sphere is:

$$\int_{\phi=0}^{\phi=2\pi} \int_{\theta=-\pi/2}^{\theta=\pi/2} f(\phi, \theta) \cos \theta \, d\theta \, d\phi \text{ watt}$$

The power flux from a uniform emitter of the same total power would be:

$$\frac{\text{Total power}}{\text{Total area}} = \frac{\displaystyle\int_{\phi=0}^{\phi=2\pi} \int_{\theta=-\pi/2}^{\theta=\pi/2} f(\phi, \theta) \cos \theta \, d\theta \, d\phi}{4\pi} \text{watt/m}^2$$

If the maximum flux is in the direction ϕ_m, θ_m then

$$\text{Gain} = f(\phi_m, \theta_m) \bigg/ \frac{\displaystyle\int_{\phi=0}^{\phi=2\pi} \int_{\theta=-\pi/2}^{\theta=\pi/2} f(\phi,\theta) \cos \theta \, d\theta \, d\phi}{4\pi}$$

$$= \frac{4\pi \times f(\phi_m, \theta_m)}{\displaystyle\int_{\phi=0}^{\phi=2\pi} \int_{\theta=-\pi/2}^{\theta=\pi/2} f(\phi,\theta) \cos \theta \, d\theta \, d\phi}$$

Appendix 2.
Radiation from Travelling-Wave Antennas

If a travelling wave originates at A (Fig.A.2) and travels to the right at a velocity V, then the field E in the wave can be described by the equation:

$$E = E_0 \sin 2\pi/\lambda \, (Vt - x)$$

where

E_0 = amplitude of field
λ = wavelength
t = time
x = distance from A.

Consider the signal at B arising from a small length of the wave dx at x, it is proportional to:

$$E_0 \sin 2\pi/\lambda \left[V\left\{ t - \frac{x + d}{c} \right\} - x \right] dx \qquad (A.2.1)$$

since the signal will have started from x at a time $(x + d)/c$

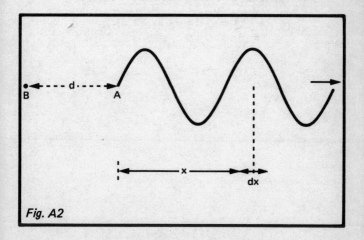

Fig. A2

before it reaches B, assuming it travels with c the velocity of light.

The signal at B from one complete wavelength will be proportional to:

$$\int_0^\lambda E_0 \sin 2\pi/\lambda \left[V\left\{ t - \frac{x+d}{c} \right\} - x \right] dx \qquad (A.2.2)$$

If the velocity of the wave along the antenna is equal to the velocity of radiation in free space, i.e. $V = c$, then A.2.2 is zero. Hence the contribution from every wavelength along the antenna is zero and there is no backward radiation.

If now B is moved to the front of the antenna then A.2.2 becomes

$$\int_0^\lambda E_0 \sin 2\pi/\lambda \left[c\left\{ t - \frac{d-x}{c} \right\} - x \right] dx$$

$$= \lambda E_0 \sin 2\pi/\lambda \left[ct - d \right] .$$

If the antenna is n wavelengths long then the forward signal is proportional to:

$$n\lambda E_0 .$$